NEIL A. KJOS
PIANO LIBRARY

W9-BOS-438

LEVEL TWO

Eugénie Rocherolle

MUSIC OF THE 21ST CENTURY

RAINBOW'S END

*For my grandchildren, Nina, Joël and Bray Deppen
and Alyssa and Annick Rocherolle, with love from "Gigi"*

CONTENTS

ISBN 0-8497-6226-X

©1997 **Neil A. Kjos Music Company**, 4380 Jutland Drive, San Diego, California 92117.
International copyright secured. All rights reserved. Printed in U.S.A.

Warning! These arrangements are protected by copyright law. To copy or reproduce them by any method is an infringement of the
copyright law. Anyone who reproduces copyrighted matter is subject to substantial penalties and assessments for each infringement.

ABOUT THE COMPOSER

Eugénie Ricau Rocherolle is widely recognized for the warm, creative musical style that reflects her personality. Her style of writing has attracted a large number of followers who are eager to learn everything she writes. She composes mostly by improvising at the piano, beginning with a basic topic or theme, and striving for contrast, humor, catchy rhythms and good melodies with appealing harmonies.

Eugénie grew up in one of this country's prominent French areas, New Orleans. Her junior year of college was spent in Paris where she studied with Nadia Boulanger. She graduated from Sophie Newcomb College of Tulane University with majors in piano and composition and was the 1995 recipient of the Newcomb College Outstanding Alumna Award. Her professional affiliations include the National Federation of Music Clubs, the Music Teachers National Association, the National League of American Penwomen, and Connecticut Composers, Inc. Her biographical profile appears in the Who's Who of American Women, Encyclopedia of Women Composers, Who's Who in the East and the International Who's Who in Music.

THE NEIL A. KJOS PIANO LIBRARY

The **Neil A. Kjos Piano Library** is a comprehensive series of piano music in a wide variety of musical styles. The library is divided into eleven levels and will provide students with a complete performance experience in both solo and ensemble music. Teachers will find the carefully graded levels appropriate when choosing repertoire for evaluations, auditions, festivals, and examinations. Included in the **Neil A. Kjos Piano Library:**

Preparatory Level - Level Ten

Piano Repertoire: Baroque & Classical
Piano Repertoire: Romantic & 20th Century
Piano Repertoire: Etudes
Music of the 21st Century
New Age Piano
Jazz Piano
One Piano Four Hands
Music for Christmas

PREFACE

Music of the 21st Century from the **Neil A. Kjos Piano Library** gives piano students of all ages and performance levels an opportunity to explore rich musical compositions by America's leading contemporary composers. In each volume, pianists are provided with an ample selection of music in a variety of tempos, keys, and styles. The carefully graded compositions ensure steady and thorough progress in contemporary styling as pianists advance. These motivational solos may be assigned for study and performance with any method or course of study.

YESTERYEAR

Eugénie R. Rocherolle

Gently ($\quad$ = 120)

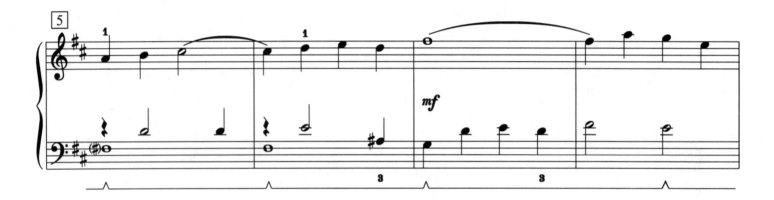

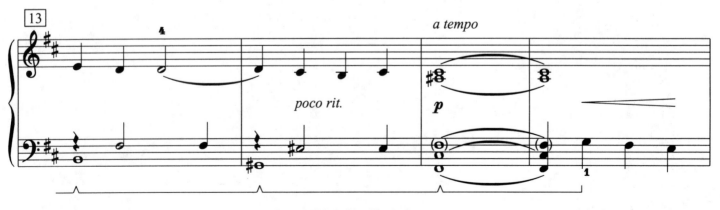

© 1997 Neil A. Kjos Music Company

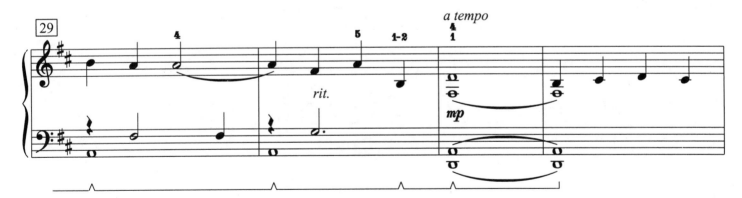

GOING GOSPEL

Eugénie R. Rocherolle

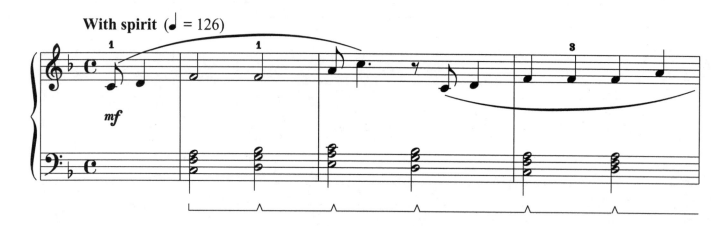

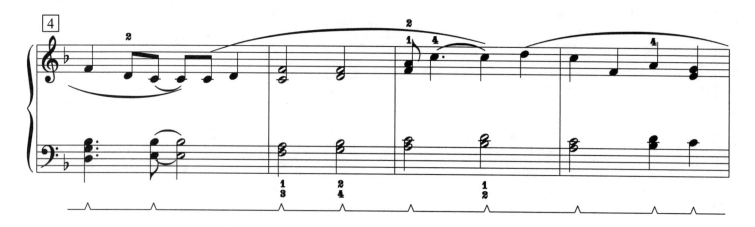

© 1997 Neil A. Kjos Music Company

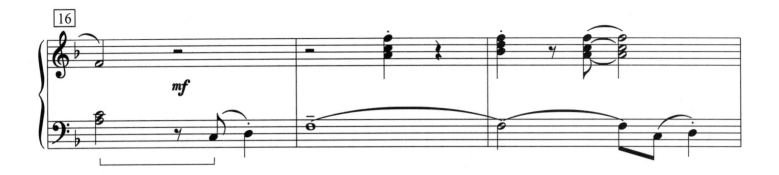

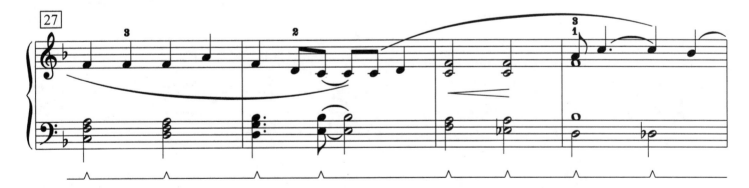

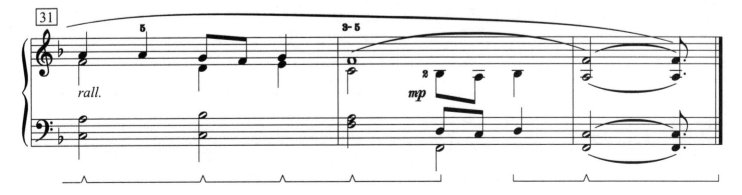

THE SULTAN

Eugénie R. Rocherolle

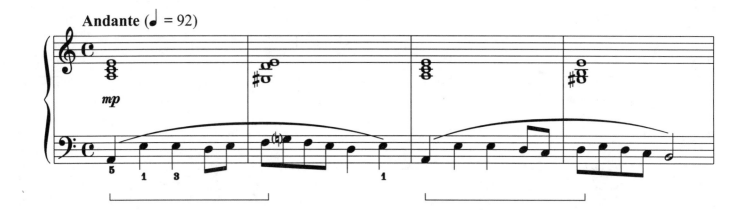

© 1997 Neil A. Kjos Music Company

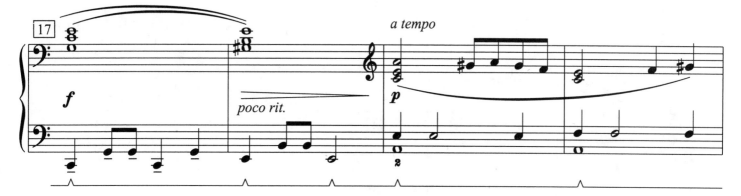

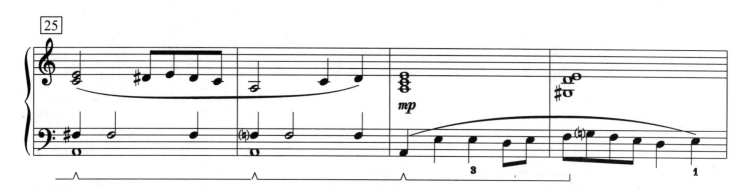

MINI WALTZ

Eugénie R. Rocherolle

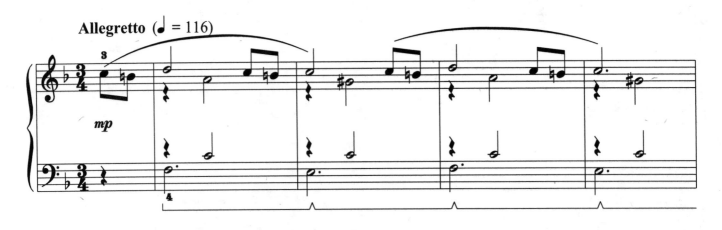

© 1997 Neil A. Kjos Music Company

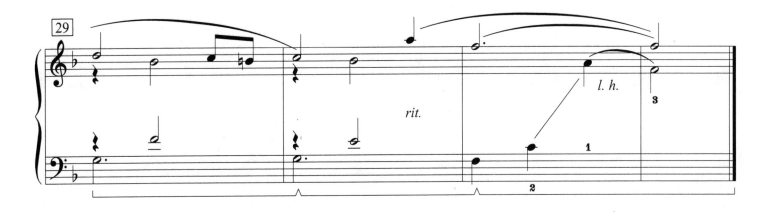

FOOTLOOSE

Eugénie R. Rocherolle

© 1997 Neil A. Kjos Music Company

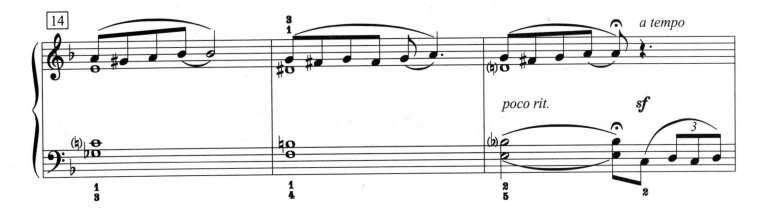

TIME ALONE

Eugénie R. Rocherolle

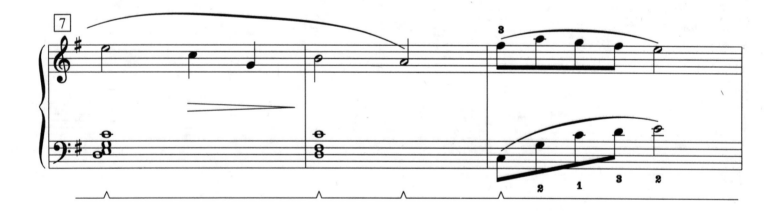

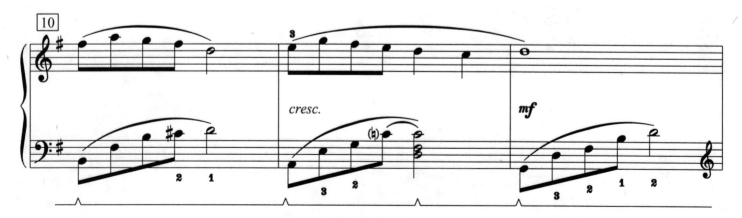

© 1997 Neil A. Kjos Music Company

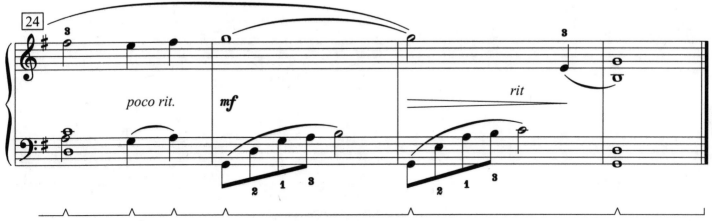

BAYOU BLUES

Eugénie R. Rocherolle

© 1997 Neil A. Kjos Music Company

ROCKY ROAD

Eugénie R. Rocherolle

With a Steady Beat (♩ = 126)

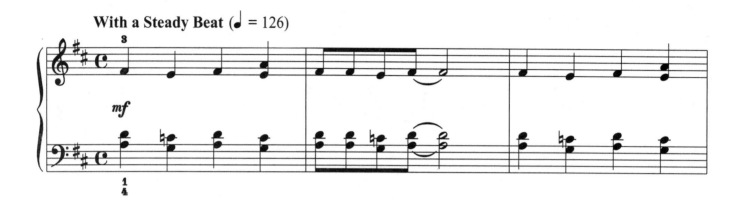

© 1997 Neil A. Kjos Music Company

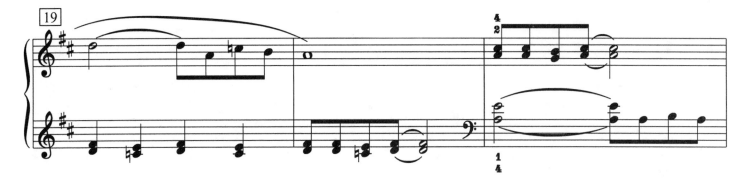

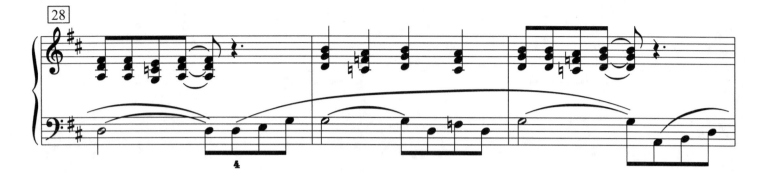

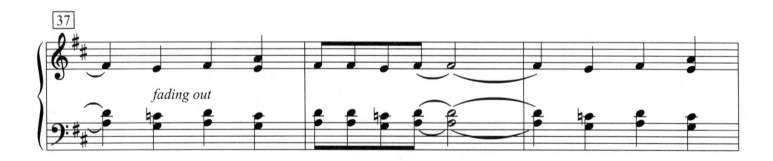

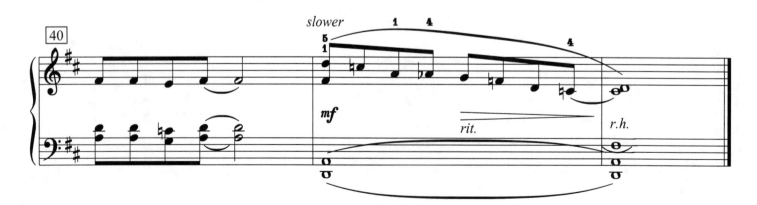

FRONTIER TOWN

Eugénie R. Rocherolle

© 1997 Neil A. Kjos Music Company

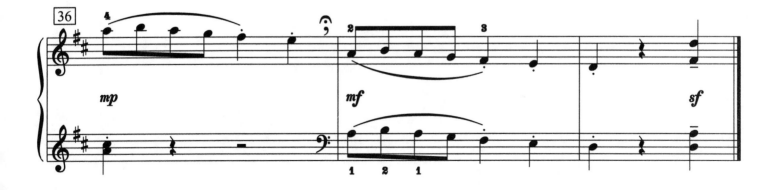